PATRICK HENRY

Voice of Liberty

Patrick Henry:

ILLUSTRATED BY LOUIS F. CARY

Voice of Liberty

WILLIAM PERCIVAL JONES

HOUGHTON MIFFLIN COMPANY

BOSTON   The Riverside Press Cambridge

Contents

CHAPTER 1

Trouble at School

Patrick Henry had just finished saying his prayers. It was a cold winter night, and the boys at Mr. Fauntleroy's Boarding School were all in their rooms. Pat was still kneeling on the drafty floor. His long woolen nightgown helped a little, but he was shivering.

The candle was out, and the log fire in the huge fireplace at one end of the room had burned down to nothing but embers. Most of the boys who shared the room with Patrick were already in bed. But as he pulled down his covers, he noticed a few of his friends huddled in front of the dying fire.

"Aren't you coming to bed?" he asked Charles Meredith, whom he recognized in the dim light.

7

"Sh-h-h." Charles put his finger to his lips. "Come here, Pat."

"What do you want?" Pat asked, still not whispering. He padded over to the fireplace. His Indian moccasins, a gift from his Uncle Langloo, the famous hunter, made soft slapping noises on the bare floor.

"Be quiet, Pat!" Sam Meriwether hissed. "Do you want to wake old 'Bag-o'-Bones'?"

"Oh, I don't care. We can all be in bed pretending to be asleep, long before he can get up the steps," Pat said, sleepily.

"I guess you'll care when you hear what we're planning to do," Charles said. "We're hungry and you must be too, after that supper tonight. I never liked fat back and greens, anyway. We know there's some venison and a ham in the kitchen, so we're going down to get some of it right now. We need you to come with us, Pat."

"No, I'm not very hungry. And suppose Old Fauntleroy caught us. He doesn't like me. This would just give him a good excuse to punish me."

"Oh, come on, Pat. He'll never catch us. Besides, what could he do about it?"

"How about Mrs. Fauntleroy? She's always snooping around."

"We'll watch."

"I don't know. If we're caught, Old Fauntleroy might not do anything to you, but I know what he'd do to me. No, gentlemen. Do what you want, but I'm going to sleep."

He turned back toward his bed.

"But Pat! We were counting on you to climb through the porch window and open the kitchen door for us. We're all too big to get through. It will open only a few inches, and all the other windows are fastened tight. The door leading to the porch is locked, but the back kitchen door has a bar on it. You can let us in that way."

The kitchen was a separate one-room building. It was connected to the main house by a narrow porch. The kitchen had a single window on the porch side.

Pat scratched his head. He was small for his nine years. His red hair was pulled

9

tightly to a pig-tail at the back of his neck. He had sharp features, with wide-set gray eyes.

"Aw, get one of the little boys to help you," said Pat, turning back to his bed. "Tom Black is much better at climbing than I am."

"But we can't trust the little boys. They might tell. Don't you see, Pat? It must be one of us. If you won't do it, none of us can go."

"Wel-l-l, all right. I'll go, but just to help you with the door."

The raid went as planned. The window was a tight squeeze, but with a few helpful pushes, Pat managed to get through. He unbarred the back door for the hungry boys. Though it was dark, they were able to cut generous slices of meat and fresh bread. They were careful to put things back exactly where they found them. Then, tiptoeing so that no one would hear them, they hurried back to their room where they could eat in safety, leaving the back door of the house open for Pat.

After the boys had gone, Pat carefully

barred the kitchen door. He had one foot through the narrow opening of the window when he heard footsteps. The dim light of a candle shone through the back door of the house onto the porch.

Mrs. Fauntleroy was coming!

Pat froze with terror. It was too late to climb back into the kitchen and hide, and he would surely be caught before he could scramble out. There was no escape. He knew that he would have to answer for the actions of all the boys.

Mrs. Fauntleroy, with the candlelight shining on her face, looked like a witch to Pat. She hurried along the porch toward the window. When she saw Pat, she scowled.

"So! There you are, you wretched boy! And what were you doing in my kitchen at this hour of the night?"

Pat was too frightened to answer.

"Well, answer me, young man! And who were the other boys with you?"

"Ma'am?" was all Pat could say.

Mrs. Fauntleroy was losing her patience.

11

"Patrick Henry! Come out here at once and I'll see whether you'll talk or not."

Patrick managed to get through the window. He stood timidly in front of Mrs. Fauntleroy, wondering what she would do next.

"And now, sir," she said, grasping his ear, "up to Mr. Fauntleroy's room with you! We'll see if we can teach little boys to behave themselves."

As she led Pat along, he was so frightened that he could hardly think. But one thing he decided, right then and there, was that he wouldn't tell about the other boys.

In his room, Mr. Fauntleroy sat tall and stern behind the big desk. Young Pat, his knees shaking, stood stiffly in front of him while Mrs. Fauntleroy told him where she had found Pat.

"Now, what do you have to say for yourself?"

"Nothing, sir. I was hungry, that's all, and . . ."

"Fiddlesticks! There was plenty of good

13

nourishing food on the table tonight! It's your own fault if you didn't eat. Who were the other boys with you?" Mrs. Fauntleroy snapped.

"Boys? What boys?" mumbled Pat, looking down at the floor.

"You know very well what I mean. I saw them running off, but I couldn't tell exactly who they were in the darkness."

"I suppose you know what I'm going to do with you, Master Henry," said Mr. Fauntleroy. "It's my duty to teach you young gentlemen to obey. Taking food that does not belong to you is stealing, you know. Stealing, do you hear?" His voice rose sharply.

"Yes, sir."

Mr. Fauntleroy was holding a four-foot switch in his hand and was dangling the switch in front of Pat.

"Now if I knew who the other boys were, your punishment would be light. If you tell me their names, I might not whip you at all. Now! Who were they?"

Pat did not reply. With a catlike bound,

14

Mr. Fauntleroy was out of his chair and at Pat's side. He took Pat by the shoulder and shook him. Pat remained silent. He could not betray his friends, no matter what the punishment might be.

Suddenly, the switch hissed sharply through the air. Pat felt the stinging burn of it on his back.

Twice.

Three times.

"Now are you going to tell me?"

"No, sir," Pat answered, trying to keep back a sob.

The switch came down again and again, but Pat would not give in.

At last Mr. Fauntleroy's anger cooled, and Pat was allowed to return to his room. His back hurt. It was hard to keep from crying, but he walked into the room dry-eyed.

It was very quiet until his friends saw that he was alone. Then they hurried over to him.

"Tell us what happened," George said in a hoarse whisper.

"Mrs. Fauntleroy caught me when I was halfway out of the window. I was so scared I couldn't move."

"Oh, Pat! What did she do?"

The boys crowded around him.

"She took me up to old 'Bag-o'-Bones'. He beat the tar out of me, just as I thought he would."

"Did you tell about us?"

" 'Course not!" There was scorn in Pat's voice. "Would you have?"

"I don't know," Sam answered honestly. "I hope not."

Pat knew that he would have trouble getting to sleep that night. He could still feel the sting of the switch on his back. He lay in bed thinking how foolish he had been to go with the other boys when he really hadn't wanted to. Just before he dropped off to sleep, he heard a whisper in the darkness. It was Charles's voice.

"Thanks, Pat. We didn't mean to get you into trouble. But we knew we could trust you."

CHAPTER 2

Uncle Langloo's Visit

In the warm spring sunshine, Virginia had never looked so beautiful. Patrick was happy. He was home for vacation and glad to be away from Mr. Fauntleroy's school.

His home was a fine old plantation, called Studley. Patrick lived there with his parents, his brother Will, some younger sisters, and his half-brother, John Syme. Although John was several years older than Patrick, they were great friends. They both loved horses, and they liked working and playing on the plantation.

One morning, as John was coming out of the stable, Patrick called to him.

"John, what's happening at the house? Everyone is out front."

"I don't know. I was just about to ask you," answered John. "Let's hurry and see what all the excitement is about."

As Pat and John ran up the path to the great house, they noticed a stranger standing on the lawn with the others. He was a tall, lean man dressed in buckskin.

"Boys!" Mrs. Henry called out to them. "Come and meet your uncle, William Winston. He has come to pay us a visit. William hasn't seen you since you were babies."

"Howdy, boys." The frontiersman reached out his strong brown hands and grasped each boy by the shoulder. "Good to see you again. But don't you dare call me Uncle William! I'm known from here to Kentucky as 'Langloo'. But to keep your mother happy, I suppose you could call me Uncle Langloo."

Pat looked up in admiration at his newly found uncle. He could hardly believe that the famous hunter he had heard so much about was really here.

William Winston was the son of a wealthy planter. He could have been living the life of a gentleman. Instead, he chose to live in the woods most of the time. Although Mrs. Henry loved her brother, she could not understand why he had chosen frontier life instead of the more comfortable and dignified life on a plantation.

"The exciting stories he must be able to tell!" thought Pat. "This is my chance to learn all about the back country."

"Come, William," Pat's mother said. "You'll want to change your clothes. Buckskins may be all right to wear in an Indian village, but here, after all —. Aaron will show you to your room and see that you have some hot water and fresh clothes."

Langloo smiled as he followed the dignified Negro into the house.

"Isn't it a shame," thought Pat. "Mother has to start off by making Uncle Langloo uncomfortable. Why can't she forget for just a minute that she is a Winston, and such a lady?"

William Winston stayed with the Henrys for nearly a month. He told many exciting tales during his visit. Since Pat loved the outdoors, he could never hear enough of his uncle's stories. He learned of the deep forest; of hostile Indians slipping from tree to tree; of how the Indians lived; and of the animals found in the wilderness.

Patrick was heartbroken when the time came for his uncle to leave.

"Won't you take me on a hunting trip, Uncle Langloo?" Pat urged.

"Well, son," said Uncle Langloo, "maybe I will some day. Perhaps after my next visit I could take you on a short trip. That is, if your parents will agree. Just now, I have to meet a friend, Lew Wetzel. We're going hunting on the Ohio, up near Zanesville. I can't take you up there with me. There are too many hostile Indians."

"Besides," added Pat's father, Colonel Henry, "you must get back to your studies in another month. That is more important for you just now than a hunting trip."

Patrick was disappointed. It didn't seem to him, at that moment, that anything could be half as important as a hunting trip with his famous uncle. But when Langloo was leaving, he promised that some day he would take both Pat and his friend Charles Dabney on a long hunting trip. Patrick was satisfied with this promise.

CHAPTER 3

Patrick Is a Hero

All the children missed their Uncle Langloo, but there were many interesting things to do at Studley. When Pat was not riding one of the fine horses, he liked to roam through the woods of the plantation. There, he and Will killed imaginary Indians by the thousands.

"Make-believe games are all right," said Pat to Will one day, "but wouldn't it be fun to have a real gun and go hunting?"

"Surely would! Maybe we could kill a deer," answered Will, happy with the idea.

"There's that old gun hanging above the fireplace in Father's study," said Pat. "It's old and no one ever uses it any more."

Without a thought for what might happen, Pat took down the old rifle and he carefully loaded it. He had often seen his father load a gun. He was surprised to find it so heavy and awkward.

Soon, the boys were walking quietly through the woods. A rustling sound made them stop suddenly. They had seen deer tracks. Now, it looked as if there were deer antlers above a thick clump of bushes just ahead of them.

Pat cocked the rifle and fired. The kick of the gun almost knocked him down. His shoulder was badly bruised. The things they had thought were antlers did not move. The boys looked at them carefully, and saw only the branches of a dead bush. The rustling sound had probably been caused by a squirrel scampering through the woods.

"Maybe I'm not ready to go hunting with Uncle Langloo yet," Pat said quietly.

Will nodded.

Pat's shoulder ached so much that the boys headed for home. They were ashamed to face their father. But Colonel Henry had heard the rifle shot. He met the boys at the door with a serious look on his face.

"You both deserve to be punished for taking the rifle without permission," he said sternly. "Rifles are not toys. You might have been killed. However, judging by your looks, I think you have learned an important lesson today. Give me your word that you'll never touch the rifle again without asking me first."

The boys gave their word, and kept it.

☆　　☆　　☆

Their sister Jane was to have a birthday soon. The boys stopped thinking of guns, and started thinking about the party. Mrs. Henry invited children from all the neighboring plantations. At last the day of the party arrived. Gallons of fruit punch were chilling in the icehouse, and Mammy Cindy, the cook, was busy making little sweet cakes.

When the party started, Mrs. Henry led games of Blind Man's Buff and Farmer in the Dell. But it soon became too hot for running games.

"Let's gather nuts," suggested Helen Meriwether, one of Jane's friends.

"Fine," said the other children, "but where shall we go?"

"There are walnut trees, hickory nut trees, and even a beechnut tree at the edge of the woods," answered Jane.

Jane gave each of her friends a basket, and in a short time the baskets were filled with nuts. They wondered what to do next. Then Charles Dabney exclaimed, "I have an idea! Let's climb trees."

"Oh, no," cried Sarah. "That's no fun."

" 'Course you can't climb in that dress, but you can watch," Sam told her.

"I have a better idea," said Pat. "Why don't I find Scipio and ask him to do some tricks for us?"

Scipio was a tall, well-built Negro boy of sixteen. He worked at the stables.

"That's a good idea," cried Sam Meriwether. "It's been a long time since I've seen Scipio. Can he still do a double somersault?"

"Just wait and you'll see," answered Pat as he hurried off to the stables.

There he found Scipio brushing one of the

horses. At first, Pat had trouble getting him to leave his work. But when he told Scipio how anxious the boys and girls were to see him do his tricks, the boy gladly followed him.

"Well, Scipio," Charles called to him. "Glad Mister Pat could find you. What are you going to do for us today? Got any new tricks?"

"Yes, sir, Mister Charles." Scipio stood on his hands and walked all around the children. Then he landed on his feet again with a spring. The children clapped.

Scipio grinned. Then he began doing back somersaults.

"You're a good acrobat, Scipio," Sam said. "You get better every time I see you. You should be in a show."

"I'd like that," Scipio said, "but I like horses, too, and besides, I belong here."

"How about doing that tree climb for us, Scipio?" Charles asked. "I've heard about it, but I've never seen you do it."

"Please, Mister Charles. I don't feel like climbing today. I almost fell the last

29

time I tried it, and now I'm a little scared."

"Oh, come on, Scipio. Don't be afraid. You can do it," said Charles, patting him on the shoulder.

"I don't know," mumbled Scipio. Then he looked at the eager faces of the children. "Well, all right."

Scipio looked at the giant limbs overhead. "This'll do," he said, as he grasped the bottom limb and quickly swung himself up to a handstanding position. "You want me to go feet first?" he called down.

"Yes," answered Charles. "Anybody can climb a tree head first."

The children were treated to a surprising sight. Scipio, standing on his hands and using his feet when he could, walked up the tree from limb to limb, with his head down all the time. The children stared in amazement as he climbed higher and higher.

"Now watch!" he shouted from the top of the tree. Scipio was doing a handstand on a small limb that grew almost straight out from the trunk. As he worked his way along the branch, it slowly bent under his weight. Suddenly there was a crack, and the branch gave way a little. For a second the children thought Scipio was going to fall, but he kept his balance. Now the branch seemed steady

enough, and Scipio kept moving out towards the end. In another instant the branch cracked again. This time, the sound was like a pistol shot. Scipio fell, head over heels, through the tightly laced branches of the giant tree. His fall was broken in ten feet by a tangle of branches. He lay there, face up, holding on with both hands.

"Scipio! Scipio! Are you all right?" called Pat anxiously from below.

Scipio did not move. He made no sound.

"Answer me, I say. Are you hurt?"

The boys and girls heard a faint sigh, but Scipio did not move.

"Listen to me," Pat called sharply. "If you aren't hurt, come down this instant!"

Scipio turned his head to one side. The children could see him trembling.

Pat was frightened, too, but he didn't waste a minute. He ripped off his shoes and coat, and began the long, slow climb to where Scipio was lying.

When he got within a few feet of Scipio, the boy turned a miserable face toward Pat.

"I don't know whether I'm hurt, Mister Pat," he groaned. "I'm too scared to move."

Pat inched himself along the limb to where Scipio was lying.

"You're going to be all right now," he said. "Nothing is going to hurt you. Come on." He held out his hand. "Let go of the branch with your left hand and take mine. Then come on down."

Scipio let go of the branch, rolled over, and almost fell. Even though he was a good acrobat, his fear kept him from using his skill. He began to pull Pat with him, but Pat held tightly to the tree with one hand and to Scipio with the other. At last Scipio got his balance.

Pat's knees were shaking so much that he could barely guide his feet as he followed Scipio down the tree. When they reached the ground, Pat sat down under the tree, breathing heavily. He was weak.

The other children were quiet. They were still a little frightened. If it hadn't been for Pat's quick thinking and courage, a terrible accident might have happened.

CHAPTER 4

Patrick Gets an Idea

When Patrick was fourteen years old, John Syme, his half-brother, was old enough to become the new master of Studley. The plantation had been left to John by his father, but the Henrys had lived there with him until he was able to take care of it by himself. Now the Henry family was free to move. Mount Brilliant, their new home, was twenty miles to the west. Although the house was plain in comparison to Studley, the Henrys were very happy to have a home of their own. The house was built in deep woods near the banks of the South Anna

River, but there was enough cleared land to make farming worthwhile.

Patrick had left Mr. Fauntleroy's school when he was ten. From that time on he had received his schooling from his father. Mr. Henry taught Latin, history, mathematics, Greek, and French to Pat, as well as to the other neighborhood boys.

Pat enjoyed Latin most of all. He admired the great Roman senators of ancient times, who were famous for their speech making. Often, when he was alone in the woods, Pat would pretend that he was a noble Roman, and that he was making an important speech. His voice would ring out clearly through the forest as he spoke in Latin, and made grand gestures.

Mrs. Henry knew of Pat's interest in orators. When the Reverend Samuel Davies came to the Forks Church nearby, Mrs. Henry thought that Pat might like to go to hear Mr. Davies preach at the Presbyterian meeting house. Pat had been going to St. Paul's, the Church of England in Hanover parish. His uncle, the Reverend Patrick Henry, preached there.

One Sunday morning, Mrs. Henry asked Pat if he would like to go to a different church that day to hear the Reverend Mr. Davies preach.

"I'd like to go," Pat answered. "Charles has heard him, and he says his sermons are the best he's ever heard."

"You can hear him and judge for yourself," his mother said. "There have been several great orators in our family, and perhaps you can become one too. While Mr. Davies is preaching, I want you to listen carefully. On the way home I will ask you to say as much of it back to me as you can."

"But Mother," Pat said, "knowing I'll have to repeat the sermon will take away the pleasure of hearing it."

"I shan't say you have to do it, my son, but I would like you to."

As Pat and his mother found seats in Forks Church, Pat was impressed by the plainness of the building. However, when the Reverend

Mr. Davies arrived and mounted the low plat-
form in front of the congregation, Pat began
to get a different impression. It no longer
mattered that he was sitting on a rough pine
bench and that the walls were not painted.

When Mr. Davies began to speak, Patrick
forgot everything else. There was dignity in
the way he talked. Mr. Davies was only
twenty-four years old. He was tall and slender and neatly dressed in a well-fitting black
suit. His white collar brought out the pale-
ness of his thin face. His large eyes shone
when he was speaking. His hands were long
and slender.

Patrick and his mother sat for a long time
after the sermon was finished. When at last
they were back in their small carriage and on
the way to Mount Brilliant, Patrick burst out
with, "Mother, I'm glad you brought me today. I've never heard anything like this before in my life. It wasn't so much what he
said, although that made sense enough. It
was the way he said it. The way he gestured
with his hands! The way his voice rang out.

And most of all, the way he looked straight at everyone. I couldn't help listening. He made me want to believe what he was saying. Some day, Mother, I would like to be as great a preacher as Mr. Davies. I'm going to practice everything I saw him do today. And I want to hear him again, soon."

And Patrick repeated almost word for word, gesture for gesture, what the Reverend Davies had given to his congregation that morning.

"I'm glad, Patrick," his mother answered. "I'll be very happy if you become a minister. But regardless of what you decide to become, the ability to sway folks with your speaking is worth the learning. Preachers are not the only ones who must know how to speak well. Lawyers and delegates to the legislature should also be orators. We'll go to hear Mr. Davies often, Patrick."

As they rode on home, Patrick dreamed of being able to speak, as Mr. Davies did, and as the Roman orators had, so that people listened and believed.

CHAPTER 5

The Hunting Trip

Patrick had been small for his age when he was younger. But by the time he was fourteen, he had grown so tall and slender that he looked awkward and walked with a slight stoop.

One sunny morning, he was out in the woods with two of the field hands clearing trees from some land that his father planned to use for that year's tobacco crop. It was hard work, and although it was still early March, the day was warm. Several times, Pat wanted to stop to rest, or go for a cool drink of water, or simply quit. But even though there were many things he would rather be doing, he knew that he must see that this work was done.

His brother Will had been working with them. But Will had already dropped his ax and slipped off into the forest.

In the middle of the morning, Pat saw a lone traveler making his way down the muddy road. He rested on his ax for a few moments to watch. The traveler was a tall man, dressed in buckskins. He was riding a handsome horse and leading a pack horse. Pat knew he had seen this man before. Who was he?

Then he knew — it was Uncle Langloo! Pat had not seen him for five years. Turning to the Negroes, he said, "You keep working. I'll be back in a little while." Pat put down his ax and bounded across the field. He stood in the road, waiting for his uncle.

Langloo slipped off his horse and greeted his red-haired nephew fondly.

"You must be Patrick, but I can hardly believe it. Last time I was here, you barely came up to my waist. I remember how you used to beg me to tell stories of the back country. And now, you're almost as tall as I am. What have you been doing out here?"

"Oh, I was just helping Ben and Mose clear a new field for the tobacco. They'll get along all right without me for a while. Will is supposed to be helping, too, but you know Will. He won't stick to anything for very long. He left his ax and is off in the woods somewhere."

"I'll see Will later. But now, let's go up to the house," suggested Langloo.

"I'll walk to the house with you, Uncle Langloo, but I mustn't stay too long. I'll have to get back out here with the field hands. Mose is all right, but I'll bet Ben is asleep under a tree right now. He always goes to sleep if you take your eyes off him for five minutes."

"All right. If you'll walk up to the house with me, I'll visit with your folks for a few minutes, and then we'll both come back. I'll take Will's ax. Tell me, how are the girls?" Langloo put his arm across Pat's shoulders as they strolled to the house.

Uncle Langloo was a wonderful man to

have around. He helped with the work and was always willing to tell exciting stories of his adventures.

One day, Pat said to him, "Uncle Langloo, I wish you would stay here forever. But when you have to go, I'd like to go with you on a hunting trip. Do you remember that you promised to take me with you some day?"

"Yes, I remember. But how about your studies? Can you take that much time away from your books?" asked Uncle Langloo.

"Oh, yes," Pat answered. "We don't do much in the summertime, anyway."

"Tell you what," Langloo said. "Let me stay a month more and be back with civilized folks again. Then, if your parents are willing, I'll take you and Charles Dabney for a two months' trip to the mountain country. When we come back, you'll be ready to settle down to your books again, and I may even spend the winter."

"Wonderful!" Pat exclaimed.

By the time Uncle Langloo had spent a month at Mount Brilliant, he was ready to return to the back country. True to his word, he took Pat and Charles with him.

They rode west to the Blue Ridge Mountains and then turned south through the valleys and rolling country. There were no Indians living in this section, Uncle Langloo explained, but hunting parties and sometimes war parties from both the north and south often passed through it. They would have to be on constant alert for unfriendly war parties and give them a wide berth.

They had made camp on the banks of a crystal stream almost in the shadow of two great mountain peaks. Uncle Langloo was building a fire to cook their evening meal while Pat and Charles gathered wood. For some reason, Pat glanced up. He was frozen in his tracks. An Indian, stern and forbidding, was standing at the edge of the glade. He was naked except for a piece of buckskin about his waist. There was a long rifle in his hands. His dark skin glistened in the last rays of the setting sun.

Patrick, to warn the others, hissed softly.

Uncle Langloo and Charles looked up and saw the Indian. They both remained motionless and silent. Uncle Langloo's hand crept slowly towards his rifle which was always within reach. Then he relaxed. His face broke into a grin.

"Well! Matko, my old friend!"

The Indian, not nearly so frightening now, strode forward. His face, too, was lit with pleasure as he greeted the white hunter. He was a chief and was leading a peaceful hunting party.

He invited Uncle Langloo and the boys to hunt with them. The chief had his own son, Chango, with him. The three boys were soon friends.

One day, Chango was teaching the boys how to stalk game, Indian fashion. The three wormed their way up the wooded hillside. Although the Indians were well supplied with rifles, powder, and ball by fur traders, the boys were hunting with bow and arrow. Pat and Charles had been practicing for years. They were good, but they didn't have the skill

47

that Chango had. Chango never missed.

The three boys were separated by a few yards. Charles was in the center and slightly in the lead, with Pat on his right and Chango on his left. Just then, Pat's hand pressed too hard on a dried twig, and it broke under the sudden weight. There was a crack that seemed deafeningly loud in the stillness of the morning forest.

Chango gestured furiously for Pat to be quiet. Pat nodded and began to move forward again. This time he took great care to be noiseless.

A little way up the slope was a place where several trees had fallen. They were lying crisscross, in a huge tangle of limbs. Chango had told them that this was just the sort of place where a deer might sleep during the day. It was a good day for stalking, for a light breeze was blowing in their faces, and the air was dry enough to cut down the scent.

Pat glanced over at Chango, who motioned slightly, pointing in the direction of the clump of fallen trees. Pat stared at it. He slowly realized that the shadow topped by curiously shaped branches was not a shadow at all. As he gazed, it became a tremendous deer, lying motionless, but with ears standing straight up and its eyes searching about. So perfectly did its color blend with the background that once when Pat took his eyes away he had difficulty finding the deer again.

Charles, Pat could see, had already spotted the deer. With his finger to his lips, Chango motioned them forward. They were within thirty paces of the deer now, good shooting distance. The deer was staring directly at Charles, and Pat felt sure they had been seen. He fitted an arrow to his bowstring, seeing as he did so that Charles was also ready to shoot.

The deer, still facing Charles, had started to rise when Charles loosed his arrow. The arrow skimmed by a twig, barely grazing the deer's shoulder but making a gash.

With an angry bellow, the buck sprang to its feet and charged. It bounded directly towards Charles, who was crouching in the open. Chango was unable to shoot because

49

Charles was directly between him and the charging deer.

Pat, with an open shot, rose to one knee and pulled the arrow back to his ear. Aiming a little ahead of the beast, he breathed a silent prayer and let the arrow fly.

Zing!

The flint tip of the arrow bit deep, burying itself in the animal halfway to the feathers.

With a final leap, the buck collapsed, falling at Charles's feet. Charles, trembling, dropped his bow and stared wide-eyed at the deer.

"Good shooting, Pat," Chango said solemnly as he walked toward the dead buck and the thoroughly frightened Charles. "You are a brave hunter. You thought fast and shot straight. There will be feasting in the camp tonight, and the chief, my father, will honor you."

CHAPTER 6

Patrick Decides
to Be a Merchant

The two months' hunting trip
with Uncle Langloo was over all too soon.
Pat had loved the out-of-doors since he was a
small boy. On this trip, taught by Langloo
and his Indian friend, Chango, Pat had become a real woodsman. During the long trip
back to Mount Brilliant, Pat was already
planning his next journey into the wilderness.

One night, a few weeks after their return,
Pat was in the parlor talking with his parents
and his uncle. The girls were in bed, and
Will was doing an errand of his own. Uncle

Langloo had a faraway gleam in his eyes.

"I wish you'd let the boy come with me on my next trip, John," he said. "There's all the land a person could ever want. In a few years, if Pat decides to settle down, he could lay out his own plantation. We need people like him in the back country."

"Oh, William," Mrs. Henry said, "isn't one barbarian in the family enough? Pat was born a gentleman, just as you were. You have chosen the frontier for your life. I could wish better things for Pat."

"You don't understand, Sarah," said Langloo patiently. "If Pat is to become a great man, it won't matter where he is. He will be none the less great in the wilderness. We need men with Pat's courage and quick thinking. After all, he'll be a man soon and should decide for himself."

"At fourteen," Colonel Henry argued, "my son is not quite a man. Later, if he wants the wilderness, he may go. I have given him a fair education. The Henrys have never been wealthy, but I have a little to give Pat for a start. We have all been dreamers and scholars. I want something better and more practical for Pat. I would like to have him learn a trade. He seems to be interested. I have already arranged for him to go into Mr. Thompson's store at New Castle as an apprentice. Even if trade proves to be the wrong job for Pat, I want him to find it out for himself. He has had experience on the plantation. You yourself have said that he is a good woodsman. To make him a well-rounded man, I think it is important that he know something about practical business dealings."

Before Pat left for New Castle, his father talked with him.

"Tell me, Patrick, have you been thinking about what you want to do with yourself? After you spend the year with Mr. Thompson, you will know how you like business. We get only enough crops from our land here to support our own family. When you and Will marry and have families of your own, we'll have to plan something else for you."

"I've thought about it a lot," Pat said seriously, "and I still don't really know what I want to do. Planting would be fine, but there's no land to be had around here. I wouldn't want to go west for just the amount of land I could work with my own two hands. You can't spare any slaves, and I have no money to buy any.

"I wanted to go to the back country, but now I think I wouldn't like to be so far away. I like to know what is going on in the towns in Virginia and the other colonies."

Patrick was fifteen when he finished his year as apprentice to Mr. Thompson. He

worked hard and faithfully, but he took no great pleasure in the work. The thing he liked best about it was listening to the talk of the country folk who gathered in the store. Sometimes Mr. Thompson was cross with him for being so interested in the talk that he would forget to wait on customers.

When Patrick's year at the store was over, he returned to Mount Brilliant. Colonel Henry asked his son if he had decided about his future.

"I like Hanover County and would like to stay here," Pat said. He was thinking of pretty Sarah Shelton. He had known her al-

most since babyhood. Last week he had stopped off at Rural Plains, her home, on his way back to Mount Brilliant. It was then he realized what a lovely girl she had become.

"Well, how about business?" his father wanted to know.

"I suppose that would be best, Father. Had I been able to go to college, I might have entered the ministry. But business will be all right for me."

"Even though you aren't sure of what you want to do, I'll tell you what I have in mind. We don't have much money to give you, but there is some. This fall, when there is not much work to be done on the plantation, we'll have some lumber sawed. Ben and Mose are pretty good with tools. We can hire a carpenter. With the help of Ben and Mose, we should be able to build you a store in no time. I've given it a lot of thought, and I believe if your store is built near where the old church road joins New Castle Road, you ought to do a good business. It will be convenient for travelers from New Castle to this part of the county, as well as being a good stopping place for people coming from New Kent and King William. We can get a little land there without any difficulty. I can give you enough money for the land, the building, and a small supply of goods."

"That will be wonderful, Father," Pat answered.

"I wish I could do more, my son. I hope you will not object to having Will for a partner. I don't know that he will be much help, but I want him to have his chance. Perhaps this will wake him up."

"Perhaps it will. Let's try anyway."

"I've already talked to John Syme and he'll be glad to have you live with him at Studley."

And so it was settled.

CHAPTER 7

Henry Brothers, Merchants

The store was built, and for a short time it did well. At first, Will was eager to learn and worked hard. After a few months, however, he began to lose interest. Some days he would be in the store a short while. On other days he wouldn't even come to the store. Patrick did not get angry with Will for not doing his fair share of the work. Instead, he bore the full load on his own sturdy shoulders.

Pat particularly enjoyed the moonlit nights. He would keep the store open, and the farmers from the small farms for miles around would come, not so much to buy as to sit and talk. There was no inn nearby, and Patrick's store was a natural meeting place. News from Williamsburg, Philadelphia, New York, and Boston, as well as the latest word from England, would find its way into the store. There was usually a ship from England tied up either at Hanovertown or New Castle.

Patrick enjoyed hearing the country people argue about the events of the day. Newspapers from England, copies of the Virginia *Gazette,* or papers from the northern colonies were milked dry of their information. Even the less important items were discussed with interest and excitement. Pat once told his sister Jane that when the House of Burgesses, which was Virginia's legislature, was in session, all he had to do was to stay in the store. By listening to his customers talk, he knew as much about what was happening as if he had been in Williamsburg.

Pat seldom took part in the talk, but he never missed a word that was said. If a group of men were seated silently in the store, Pat would start them talking. Sometimes he would do this by asking what they thought about some subject of interest. At other times, he would start an argument by saying something with which he knew they would not agree. Then someone would take Pat's side in the argument, and Pat would sit quietly by, listening.

In this way, Patrick learned exactly what the people believed in. He knew what they thought and what they stood for. Ever since he had been a small boy he had heard his father, his uncle, and their friends discuss the affairs of the day. He had been a visitor at almost all of the great houses in the county and he had heard the talk of many people. Now he was learning what the woodsmen, the small farmers, and the workmen thought.

One afternoon in his store, Pat was listening to a lively discussion about the price of tobacco. The crop in parts of the county would be small that year. The price of tobacco would be very high. It was the custom in those days to pay parsons of the

Church of England in tobacco rather than in money.

With this in mind, one of the men complained bitterly that the parsons would continue to get their 16,000 pounds of tobacco, even though its value in money might be several times more than usual.

"It's a shame," said the man. "When times are hard, the parsons' salaries should be cut. This way they are being paid three or four times over."

Pat had to leave the discussion when Jake Travillian entered the store. Jake farmed a few acres of land nearby and had a houseful of children.

"Evenin', Mister Henry," he said.

"Hello, Jake. What can I do for you?"

"Well," Jake answered, "first of all I need a needle, a peck of salt, a jug of molasses, and, oh yes, my wife asked me to get her two yards of calico."

"Certainly, Jake." Pat gathered the articles quickly and then lowered his voice so that the other men could not hear him. "Say,

64

Jake, I hate to say anything about this, but could you pay me a little money? Your bill is quite high, and I just can't carry you and all my other friends much longer. I owe money too. When I sell goods in the store, I have to buy new things. These things have to be paid for. If people don't pay me in

cash when they buy things, then the day is going to come when I won't have enough money to buy anything to sell, and I'll be out of business."

"I reckon it is hard on you, Mister Pat. I hadn't thought about it that way. I have no money at all, just my tobacco patch that's comin' along fine. But I don't want to be the cause of your ruin. I just won't take this stuff. We'll make out somehow, and you'll have first choice of my tobacco, Mister Pat. Don't you worry about it. Don't you worry about it one bit."

Jake started to leave the store.

"No, Jake. Wait a minute. I didn't mean that." He hesitated for an instant. "Take the things, man. I know you'll pay me when you can. In the meantime, I'll be all right. You just work that tobacco patch. And I'll tell you what. I'll throw in some rock candy for the children."

Pat watched from the store porch as Jake left. He mounted his ancient horse and with his bags perched on the animal's back he rode off with a grateful wave of his hand. As Pat went back into the store, he found that he was being stared at by the two men who had remained seated inside. They must have overheard the conversation, even though Pat had tried to keep his voice low.

"Pat Henry," one of them said, "you know mighty well that unless it rains and rains soon, Jake isn't going to have much of a tobacco crop, and neither is anyone else."

"I know," Pat said wearily, "but he had to have his molasses and salt. I'm sure his wife needed calico, or she wouldn't have asked him for it. The problem isn't just around here, but all over Virginia. If the tobacco crop is small here, it will be small everywhere, and tobacco will be worth more. Things will work out somehow."

CHAPTER 8

Patrick Wins
a Wife

Things did not work out for Patrick. His store, The Henry Brothers, Merchants, had been in business for exactly one year when he was forced to close it. His customers owed Patrick money which they were unable to pay him. And Patrick, in turn, owed money to people from whom he had bought goods to sell to his customers.

Pat, therefore, returned what goods he had left to the people from whom he had bought them to help pay his debts. By the time his bills were paid, there was nothing left.

Patrick did not turn to his father, since he

knew full well that Colonel Henry could not afford to help him again.

When John Syme heard about Pat's difficulty, he was quick to offer aid.

"How much do you need, Pat? I know that you'll collect the money that is due you, sooner or later. I'm not really risking anything. I had a good tobacco crop last year, and I may do all right this year. Would a few thousand pounds of tobacco help?"

Pat looked at his half-brother fondly.

"Thank you, John," he said, "more than I can ever tell you. But I'll not take your money. I have to face the truth. I'm just not meant for the trade. If I took your money, I'd just lose that, too. But if you'll let me, I'd like to stay here at Studley for a while. It will take some time to settle the affairs of the store, and if I'm here I'll have more chance to collect what is owed to me than if I go back to Mount Brilliant. I don't know what Will's going to do. I suppose he'll go back to Mount Brilliant now."

"Of course you can stay here," John assured him. "Stay as long as you wish. Mildred and I are getting married in a couple of months, as you know, but that won't change anything. She thinks as much of you as I do.

"What do you plan to do when you clear up all your business at the store?"

"I don't know," Pat said. "I've known for at least two months that we couldn't hang on much longer at the store. If we could have kept things going until the harvest, and if it had been a good one, perhaps we might have managed a little while longer. But I'm sure now that I'll never be a *real* merchant. I like people too much. When they need something, and I have it, I can't help giving it to them, even though I know they can't pay. There must be something I can do well. Perhaps I'll go to the back country with Uncle Langloo."

It took Patrick nearly a year to settle the affairs of the store. During those months, he spent more of his free time at Rural Plains, the nearby home of the Sheltons, than he did at Studley. There were dances at Rural

Plains and at other homes in the area, and whenever there was a dance, Patrick was sure to be there. He was gay and fun-loving. Everybody liked him.

When Sarah Shelton was at a dance, Patrick could see no one else. He thought her the most beautiful girl in Virginia and knew that he wanted to marry her some day.

One summer evening when he was at Rural Plains, Patrick and Sarah were walking in the garden. The moon was just rising above the treetops. They paused to look at it. Suddenly, Pat found himself looking at Sarah, instead of the moon. Her blond hair was especially pretty in the moonlight. He had never seen her looking lovelier.

"Sarah," he said, "if only we could get married. But I just can't marry now. What are we going to do?"

Smiling, Sarah asked, "Why can't you marry me now?"

"You know as well as I. I have no money, no land, and no job."

"That doesn't matter. I happen to love

72

you, Pat Henry, and we'll get along. I know
we will. Come with me. We'll talk to Father
and see what he has to say."

Mr. Shelton didn't seem at all surprised
when Sarah and Patrick told him they wanted
to get married.

"I want to marry Sarah more than anything in the world," Pat said, "but, as you know, I have no money, and at the moment no job."

"I know that, Pat," Mr. Shelton said, "but you are just eighteen, and I'll be glad to help you as much as I can. I'm sure your father will too. I have six slaves I can give you, as well as the Pine Slash farm. I always planned to give the farm to Sarah when she got married. The house isn't much, but perhaps your father and I can have some work done on it. As a matter of fact, Colonel Henry and I have already discussed the matter. Long ago we decided that when you two wanted to get married, we would give you all the help we could."

Both Pat and Sarah were overjoyed. In a few moments they went back to the garden. As they strolled hand in hand, Pat said slowly, "You know, Sarah, I'm not very proud of the experience I had in the store. We could have done well, I'm sure of it, if people had been able to pay us what they owed. I know the farm will be different."

74

He grinned. "Guess we'll have to call it a farm, too. It certainly isn't big enough to be called a plantation."

"It will be wonderful to have a house of our very own, Pat. We'll save our money and buy more land. Many of the rich planters started in a small way, and we can, too."

"I didn't make a good merchant," said Pat, shaking his head. "Perhaps I can make a good planter. I helped Father manage Mount Brilliant for several years, and I've helped John these past two years at Studley. I'll work hard. We'll make things work out all right."

"Of course we will, Pat," Sarah said, squeezing his hand warmly and smiling up at him.

A short time later, Patrick and Sarah were married and settled down on the farm. Pat worked long hours with his field hands, getting the first tobacco crop started. It was back-breaking work, but he did it gladly. It was for Sarah, for their new home, and for their children to come.

75

CHAPTER 9

A Christmas Party

In a small way the farm was successful. Pat and Sarah were very happy together. They worked hard, and the years passed quickly. They had been married for six years, and they had children of their own.

It was Christmas, and friends for miles around were gathered at Colonel Dandridge's plantation. In the drawing room, the Henrys were surrounded by ladies who were talking about their children. Patrick was not too interested in all this talk of babies. He slipped away and wandered into the library, where he found several gentlemen having some punch while they talked about the affairs of the day.

Pat, having been invited to join them, sat quietly in a corner, sipping a cup of punch and listening to their conversation. As usual, he made no effort to take part, but was content to learn all he could from the talk of others.

Mr. Morgan was talking about how unfair England was to the colonies. Some of the English leaders wanted to get as much money as possible out of the colonies. The colonists were forced to buy certain things from England, even if it would be cheaper and easier to make many of these things in America and sell them to one another.

Two other gentlemen, Mr. Pendleton and Mr. Maury, didn't think this unfair. They argued that since Virginia and the other colonies were England's colonies, the King or his representatives could rule them as they saw fit. The colonists simply had to obey.

The argument grew hot and heavy. Finally, Mr. Morgan turned to Patrick.

"And what, sir, do you think about this matter?"

"Sir and gentlemen," Patrick answered, "I am embarrassed to be called on to give my poor opinions to so brilliant a gathering. But since you ask me, I must agree with you. There is a matter that both His Majesty and the Parliament seem to have forgotten. We are free-born Englishmen. The fact that our parents, grandparents, or even more distant ancestors chose to move to these shores makes us nonetheless Englishmen. The King and Parliament seem to feel that we are here only to make money for the Mother Country. Their actions are making us slaves."

"Hear! Hear!" The applause of many of the gentlemen echoed from the walls. Patrick Henry was only twenty-three, but as he spoke, these gentlemen listened to his words.

"But we are not slaves! As Englishmen, we should have all the rights of free-born Englishmen!"

"But what are you going to do about it, boy? Eh? What are you going to do about it?" asked Mr. Chiswell, an elderly gentleman known for his sharp tongue.

"I don't know, sir," Pat answered. "The time will come when all of us will have to decide. But this I do know. I, for one, will not accept slavery easily."

Amid the talk that followed this speech, a Negro servant, handsomely dressed in scarlet and buff, announced dinner. As the gentlemen were leaving the room to join their wives, old Mr. Chiswell gave Pat's elbow a firm squeeze.

"And whose ideas were those, my young friend?" he asked. "Those of your father, or your own?"

"My own, sir," Patrick answered.

"Then I should like to talk to you some more, Mr. Henry."

Pat found Sarah and joined the other guests as they strolled toward the dining room. Two sideboards and a huge table were laden with a young pig which had been roasted whole, platters of quail, a wild turkey, venison, and oysters, scalloped and raw.

Mrs. Dandridge came across the room toward Pat and Sarah. With her was a slender young man who was sixteen or seventeen.

She smiled at the Henrys and said, "Oh, there you are! Here is a young guest, just arrived, whom I would like you to meet — Mr. Thomas Jefferson, of Albemarle. He is on his way to the College of William and Mary, and he is going to spend Christmas with us."

Sarah gave the young man a sweeping curtsy. He bowed to her, and then shook hands with Pat.

Mrs. Dandridge moved on to talk to her other guests.

Tom Jefferson smiled warmly at Pat and Sarah and said, "I've been told you are among the most popular couples in Hanover, and I can well believe it."

Sarah smiled and thanked the young man.

"And how do you find the work at William and Mary?" Pat asked.

"I don't know," Tom answered with a grin. "I'm just beginning. I hope to study law under Professor Wythe. I am told he's a brilliant man."

"Our hostess tells me you play both the violin and the flute," Tom said to Pat.

"She is much too kind," Pat answered.

"From what she said, you're very good indeed. I like to play the fiddle, too. Do you play an instrument, Mistress Henry?"

"The harpsichord, sir. I often play with Patrick."

"How wonderful! Perhaps we can get together for a little music after dinner. I have my fiddle with me, and I have seen Madam

Dandridge's harpsichord. Do you have an instrument with you, sir?"

"I have both my violin and my flute. Now, since you play the violin," Pat added with a smile, "I think it might be just as well if I play the flute this evening. That way I may avoid being shown up as the poor musician I really am."

Tom Jefferson grinned.

After dinner, they found the parlor empty, so Pat, Sarah, and Tom settled down to play for a while. It was not long, however, before the other guests had gathered to listen. The trio entertained the group until the hired musicians arrived to play for dancing.

CHAPTER 10

Patrick Makes a Decision

One spring night, Pat and Sarah had not been asleep for long when Sarah awoke. She sat up in bed and sniffed. Quickly she shook her husband.

"Pat! Pat! Wake up. I smell smoke."

Patrick rubbed his eyes sleepily.

"Smoke?" he asked. Suddenly, he sat up, too. "You do! Quick. See to the children. I'll try to find the fire."

Pat ran down the stairs. The fire was coming from the kitchen. The whole room was in flames, and Pat could see at a glance that it would be useless to fight the fire.

Dashing back up the stairs, he found Sarah

and said, "Let's get the children out quickly. Then I'll come back and see what can be saved. You run to the cabins and tell Amos to get some people here as quickly as possible. We can't save the house, but we can save some of the furniture."

Sarah had the youngest child in her arms and had already started down the stairs as Pat sent the other children after her. He gathered up an armful of blankets and clothes, and followed his family out to a safe distance from the house.

Then Patrick rushed into the smoke-filled house and began throwing clothing and anything else he could from the upstairs windows. Amos and the other field hands arrived, and with their help, Pat saved whatever he could before the fire spread through the whole house.

Sarah was seated on a blanket with the children as she watched Patrick and the Negroes make a brave effort to save her belongings. When nothing more could be done, Patrick came over and sat beside her.

The house had burned to the ground. The children, wrapped in blankets, had fallen asleep. As Sarah looked at what was left of their home, she broke into tears. Pat comforted her as best he could.

"What are we going to do now?" she asked.

Pat didn't know, but he didn't sit and worry for long. He made himself smile brightly at Sarah.

"I don't know, but we will find a way to work things out. Right now, we must find some shelter for the night. The barn is warm, and we can sleep on the hay. By morning, things will seem brighter."

The next morning, they moved into a small overseer's house. Sarah's father had bought the inn at Hanover Court House the year before. When the weather got cold, they moved into the inn. Pat rode over to Pine Slash every day to keep the farm running.

Looking for a way to earn more money, Pat opened another store. To raise the money to do this, he had to sell some of their property. He rented a building, bought some goods, and once again became a merchant as well as a planter. He hired a clerk to help in the store.

Patrick and Sarah had great hopes that now their luck would change for the better. Again they were disappointed. That year turned out to be a bad one for tobacco. Pat's own crop was small. But worse than that, his customers had poor harvests and were unable to pay their bills. Before the year was up, this store had to be closed, also.

"Sarah," Pat said in a discouraged voice, "why does everything I try to do turn out badly? I have had one failure after another. Surely there must be something I can do well!"

"Of course there is, my dear," Sarah said patiently. "All you have to do is keep trying and you will find it."

"Then pray I find it soon! I'm tired of seeing you and the children live such a hard life. For all the back-breaking work on the farm we get so small a harvest. And it isn't right for your father to have to support us and even give us the roof over our heads. There must be something I can do. There has to be!"

Sarah was thinking while Pat continued to blame himself for not making a good living for his family. There was a faraway look in her eyes. Suddenly she interrupted him.

"Patrick, I have an idea. Your father gave you a good education. You know Latin, Greek, and mathematics. You love to talk about things, and at times you can be most persuasive. People listen when you speak. You have a grand way with words and a wonderful way of gesturing with your hands. You must study law, Pat. You were meant for it!"

"Law? The idea never occurred to me."

"Let's plan to visit Mount Brilliant soon and discuss it with your father. Since he is a justice, he will be able to advise you," Sarah said excitedly.

At Mount Brilliant, a few days later, Colonel Henry heard their idea. He had been disturbed about Patrick's past failures, so he listened with great interest to everything that his son and Sarah had to say.

Sarah's eyes were sparkling with excite-

ment as the family talked it over. Patrick's mother became almost as excited as Sarah.

"My dears," Mrs. Henry said, "it's a wonderful idea. Patrick will make a fine speaker. When I used to take him to church when he was a child, he could repeat almost the entire sermon on the way home. Sometimes he sounded better than the parson."

Colonel Henry smiled at his wife's remark, and then turned to Patrick.

"First, Son, you will have to spend some time reading law. Then you will have to go to Williamsburg to get your license to practice. The examination you must pass to get a license will not be easy. It would be best if you could work as a clerk in a law office while you are studying, but since you have a family to take care of, that won't be very practical. Instead, you will have to get some good books and study by yourself. I have an extra copy of the Virginia Code, and I think that Edmund Pendleton may lend you a book or two. Between us we can probably give you the help you will need."

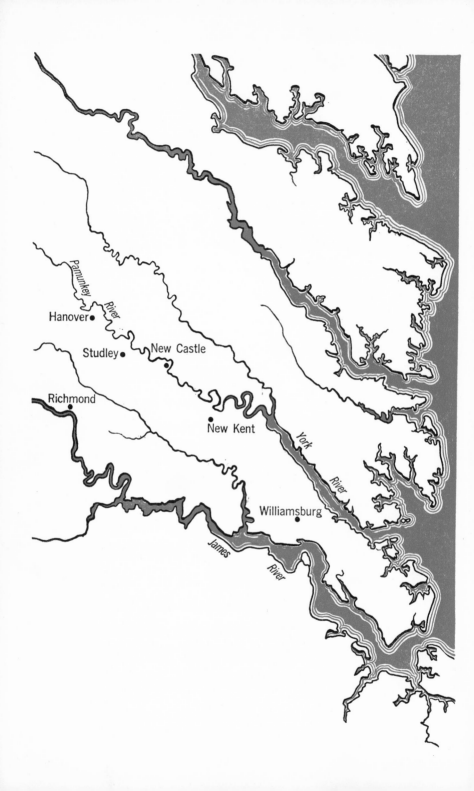

CHAPTER 11

Patrick Henry, Attorney

For eight months, Patrick did two jobs. He ran the farm, and he studied law. By working the farm in the daytime, he made money to take care of his family. At night, he studied law. He got help with his studying whenever he could, but most of the time he had to work alone.

On the last day of March, 1760, twenty-four-year old Patrick Henry set out for Williamsburg to take his examination. He felt that he couldn't wait any longer to begin to practice law. The winter had been a hard one, and spring was late in coming. This last day of March was raw and windy, with sudden rain storms. The roads were deep with mud. Before his arrival in New Castle, Pat rode through a downpour. Rain beat through the threadbare coat he was wearing, and the wind whipped the skirts of the coat around his legs.

Patrick had never cared much about clothes. To be clean and fairly neat was all that had ever mattered to him. During the three years since the house had burned, Patrick had had no new clothes. He rode the highway to Williamsburg looking more like a scarecrow than a young man who would become famous.

Patrick spent the night at an inn in New Kent and arrived in Williamsburg the next afternoon. He was impressed by the splendid shops he saw there. They were nothing like his own simple backwoods stores. The homes on the Duke of Gloucester Street were the finest he had ever seen. As he passed the Bruton Church, he paused on the palace green to stare at the magnificent home of the

Royal Governor. He did not dream that one day he would live in this house as the first governor of a free Virginia.

Patrick took a room in one of the small inns and then went looking for Tom Jefferson.

Patrick's return to Hanover was very different from the trip away from there. On his ride back the birds were singing and a warm sun was shining. It was the first real spring day. If the weather alone were not enough to make him happy, he had in his pocket a license to practice law.

When Patrick reached the inn, he left his tired horse with the stable boy. With his saddlebags over one arm, he climbed the broad steps. He looked up to see Sarah waiting at the top. He put on a glum expression.

"Tell me, Pat, is it good news or bad?"

"Oh, Sarah, the examination was hard, very hard. The examiners knew so much, and I so little."

"Do you mean they didn't pass you?" Sarah looked unhappy.

"Well, Mr. Nicholas refused to examine me." Now there was a twinkle in Pat's eye. "Mr. Wythe and Mr. Randolph said I would certainly have to read more law, but," he paused, "they signed my license anyway."

He smiled happily. Dropping the saddlebags, he lifted Sarah into the air and swung her around and around. When he put her down, they were both breathless.

"Here it is — my license to practice law. I can begin tomorrow."

"Oh, Pat. I'm so glad. Tell me all about it."

The children gathered around, happy to see their father. After greeting each of them, Patrick began his story.

"The first thing I did was find Tom Jefferson. I told him why I had come, and he was glad to help. He introduced me to Mr. George Wythe with whom he was very friendly.

"Mr. Wythe asked me a few questions about English common law, and about the laws of Virginia. Then he signed my license. I'm afraid he signed more as a favor to Tom than

96

because he thought very much of either my knowledge or appearance." Pat looked down at his clothes. "But no matter why, he did sign.

"The next morning I called on Mr. Nicholas, a great lawyer. He took one look at me and suggested I go back to my plowing. He said there were too many ragtags and bob-tails who were lawyers already, and he wouldn't think of adding another. He refused to examine me.

"That afternoon I went to see Mr. John Randolph, the King's Attorney. I was frightened as I was shown into his office. But my experience with Mr. Nicholas had taught me a lesson. This is what I did.

" 'Mr. Randolph,' I said as I entered his office, and before he had a chance to do more than glance at me, 'I am well aware, sir, that my appearance leaves much to be desired. I believe, however, that clothes do not make the man, and that my looks have nothing to do with my ability as a lawyer. Sir, I have been reading law and I have come to Williamsburg to get a license to practice. Mr. Wythe has signed my license. Mr. Nicholas refused to examine me.'

"Mr. Randolph then gave me a harder examination than any I ever dreamed of. I may have missed questions on the law, but when he started an argument about the Two Penny Act, things went much better. I have heard Father, Uncle Patrick, and other men talk about it a great deal, and I have thought about it myself. He must have liked what I said because when we finished, he complimented me and signed my license."

Patrick was greatly pleased. This time, he felt sure that he would not fail. He had found something that he could do well.

CHAPTER 12

The Twopenny Acts

Patrick began the practice of law without delay. Work came to him almost immediately. Everyone in the county knew him and liked him. He had many clients. For the first time in their married life, Patrick and Sarah had enough money to live comfortably. They were able to pay Sarah's father for their rooms and meals at the inn.

One evening after supper, Pat and Sarah were sitting on the porch.

"I understand," she said, looking pleased, "that you are going to defend the Louisa church people in the case brought to court by the Reverend Mr. Maury. Why did Mr. Lewis give up the case?"

"Mr. Lewis felt that there was no chance of winning it."

"Then why did you take it?"

"Because they asked me to. I have to make a name for myself. If I should win this case, it would do me a great deal of good. If I lose it, it will not hurt me because people will say it was lost when I took it. In the case of John Lewis, he already has a reputation. He does not want to do anything to spoil it. Besides," he added with a grin, "we are not so rich yet that I can afford to turn down any case that comes to me."

"But Patrick, why are the people of Louisa refusing to pay Mr. Maury his money?"

"I'll try to explain it as simply as I can, Sarah. In Virginia, as you know, the value of tobacco changes a little from year to year, depending on the size of the crop. Since most people use tobacco instead of money, this is important. Usually the change is slight, but sometimes when there isn't enough rain, and

102

the crop is very small, the price of tobacco can double or even triple. That means that a man who pays a debt in tobacco will be paying twice or even three times the amount of money he actually owes.

"The lawmakers in Virginia decided to do something to protect the people when the price of tobacco changes like this. Several years ago, when there was a bad drought, the tobacco crop was very small. When the House of Burgesses met, our lawmakers passed the first Twopenny Act. This law fixed the price of tobacco at two pennies a pound. This way, people bought and sold things at usual prices, rather than very high or very low prices, depending on the crop.

"After ten months, things were back to normal, and the Twopenny Act was not needed any more. But several years later, there was another poor crop and the Twopenny Act was passed again.

"The parsons thought the Twopenny Acts were unfair and were keeping them from getting all the salary they were supposed to get.

103

They sent a minister to King George to persuade him to remove these Acts. The King did so. But the King shouldn't have done this. He was not considering the good of the colony. If we passed these laws, we must have felt the need for them. We are a self-governing colony, and can make wiser laws for ourselves than will any king from across the Atlantic.

"But now that the King has said that the Twopenny Acts were never laws, the parsons want to collect the pay they didn't get during those two years when the Twopenny Acts were in effect.

"Two parsons have already gone to court to try to collect the money. One of them won his case; the other lost. Now Mr. Maury's case is coming up in the Hanover Court. Most people think he will win. That is why Mr. Lewis decided not to take the case.

"But I intend to fight this case as long and as hard as it is necessary. I understand the parsons' point of view, but I believe in the people's cause. The parsons and the King want their own way. But I believe that, in fairness, the people's claim is more right and just.

"Mr. Maury is a fine man and a good preacher. But he is standing for all the preachers against the people. The people just can't afford to pay their preachers three times their usual salaries. That is what Mr. Maury would force them to do. A wrong is being done, and if it is within my power, I am going to correct it."

CHAPTER 13

An Important Case

The day of the trial finally came. From his window, Patrick watched the people collecting on the green in front of the courthouse. They were mostly backwoods people, many of them from Louisa. They came on hungry-looking horses, or in wagons and gigs.

"These people from the farms and country plantations are the backbone of this colony," he thought. "They are beginning to object to the harsh way that England is treating them. Most of the people believe that they should make their own laws. They believe that they should not be forced to accept the laws made for them by a stubborn king and a group of greedy men in England who have never seen a tobacco field dry up in a drought, or known the danger and hardship of life on the frontier."

At last it was time to go to court. Pat was nervous, for not only was this an important case, but in addition, his father was one of the justices. The young lawyer did not know then that before the day was over his father would be very proud of him.

As Pat crossed the road, he was disturbed to see his Uncle Patrick, a highly respected minister, drive up.

"Good morning, sir," Patrick said, looking a bit uncomfortable.

"Good morning, Patrick," his uncle said, smiling. "I am very sorry you took this case. Mr. Lewis is an able and respected lawyer, and he gave it up as a lost cause. I hate to see you take a case that can only bring discredit to you. You cannot possibly win. But since you are foolish enough to try the impossible, I will be praying that things do not go too badly."

"Thank you for the offer of prayer, Uncle Patrick," Pat replied. "I shall need it. But I would rather you prayed for me at home. Just knowing you are in the courthouse will disturb me. This is not a lost cause. I'm going to try very hard to win. Some harsh things may be said about the parsons. That's another reason I'd rather you didn't come to the trial."

"Very well, Patrick," he said. "I'll go back home."

With a nod of his head and a wave of his hand, the Reverend Patrick Henry clucked to his horse and started back toward his home. The lawyer, Patrick Henry, breathing a grateful sigh of relief, made his way through the crowd into the courtroom.

Pat sat at a table with one of the Louisa collectors who had come to represent his church group in court. On a long bench near the front of the courtroom sat twenty parsons. They were among the best educated and the most powerful men in the colony. Pat

shivered as he looked at them. He was thankful that his uncle wasn't there.

Mr. Peter Lyons, who was the Reverend Mr. Maury's lawyer, thought that his case was as good as won. After all, the King of England had done away with the Twopenny Act, and the colonists had no right to argue about that. In a very casual manner, he presented his case. He told how Mr. Maury had been paid in cash in 1758, when the Twopenny Act was in effect. Mr. Maury had been paid at the rate of two pennies a pound, though tobacco was worth more than three times that amount in that year.

"You see, gentlemen," said Mr. Lyons, "Mr. Maury and his family have been robbed of two hundred sixty-four pounds sterling! The King has removed the Twopenny Act, so the church people must, according to law, pay the full value of 16,000 pounds of tobacco. The law is plain, and the facts are simple. There is nothing more to say about it. I rest my case."

Now Patrick rose to his feet. He seemed frightened and nervous as he bowed to the justices and turned toward the jury. He looked so awkward standing there, that some of the ministers laughed. The people who had come to hear the case doubted that this young man of twenty-seven could be of much help to them.

Quietly, Pat presented the receipt, signed by Mr. Maury, for his salary of one hundred thirty-six pounds sterling, paid in 1758. Then Patrick began his argument. As he started to speak, a wonderful change came over him. He straightened his shoulders and held his head high. He seemed to tower over everyone in the room. His gray eyes flashed at his audi-

ence, and the people felt great strength and force behind his words. So clearly did he speak that even his softest whisper could be heard everywhere in the room.

In clear, ringing tones, Pat spoke of the rights of Englishmen.

"For centuries, there has been an agreement between the King and his people. The King is sworn to protect his people, and the people, for their part, are sworn to obey the Crown. The Twopenny Act was a good law. It was a necessary law, vital to the well-being of the colony. It did apply to the salary of the parsons, but it applied equally to all debts. Had it not been in effect, our colony would have been ruined. A king who wanted to protect his people would not have removed it!"

The parsons were stunned by these fiery words. They began to look concerned. They had heard that this Patrick Henry was just a young upstart who was a beginner in law, and had never spoken to a large audience before. The country people began to look much happier. They listened eagerly as Patrick continued.

"The parsons, by right, ought to be ministers unto their people. In attempting to force payment of money to which they were not really entitled, they have become enemies of the community! In the case now before you,

114

Mr. Maury should not be paid. Rather, he deserves to be punished! Unless you, gentlemen, wish to put chains about your own necks, you will not lose this opportunity.

"An example must be made of Mr. Maury that will hereafter be a warning to him and to his brother parsons. They should not seek to destroy laws passed by the House of Burgesses. This House represents all the people of Virginia. Only laws passed by it can, in justice, be used to govern our colony. A king, by removing a law such as this one, stops being a father to his people, concerned about their safety and well-being. He becomes a tyrant and loses all right to the people's obedience!"

Patrick paused. He looked at people's faces. He saw that some were delighted to hear such rebellious talk. Others were shocked; others were angry. A murmur of "Treason, treason," could be heard. Speaking against the King was, indeed, treason.

Pat went on, fearless. He turned to the jury and asked if these ministers, who were supposed to be filled with goodness and unselfishness, really practiced what they preached.

"No, gentlemen!" Patrick's voice thundered through the courtroom. "Instead of feeding the hungry and clothing the naked, this pack of wolves, were they able to do what they want, would snatch from the hearth of their honest people the last hoecake; from the widow and her orphaned children, their last cow, and the last blanket from the new-born baby!"

Pat's voice dropped to almost a whisper.

"Gentleman, I need say no more. Under the law, since the Act of 1758 was cancelled by the King, Mr. Maury has to win this case. You will have to decide this case in favor of Mr. Maury, I repeat. But the damages you award him need be no more than one penny!"

With a bow to the jury and the justices, Pat went back to his seat. The jury left the courtroom. In less than five minutes they returned to say that Mr. Maury had won his case. Then they ordered the church collector to pay him exactly one penny!

A cheer went up from the people in the courtroom, and Patrick was carried out on the shoulders of his delighted countrymen.

CHAPTER 14

The Stamp Act Speech

During the next few years, Patrick Henry became one of the most sought-after lawyers in the colony of Virginia. Success brought more success. When a person does one thing well, he is likely to do other things well. So it was with Patrick. As he gained experience, he became a famous and powerful lawyer. His fame had even reached England, and he was known as one of the best colonial lawyers.

In the spring of 1765, Patrick was elected to the House of Burgesses. He was excited as he rode into Williamsburg to take his seat in the House. He was entering a new world.

While the House was meeting, news came from England that the Stamp Act had been passed by Parliament. The colonies had complained that an act of this sort was unjust. The Stamp Act required that a tax stamp be put on many articles, such as newspapers, legal papers, and even calendars. To make matters worse, the stamps had to be paid for with gold or silver money, and there was very little of either in the colonies. To many colonists, this Stamp Act was just another way to wring money out of them. But most of the older burgesses felt that there was nothing they could do about it.

The House of Burgesses went on with its business. Most of the bills were unimportant, including one that would keep the citizens of the new town, Richmond, from allowing their pigs to run loose in the streets.

Patrick thought about the Stamp Act a great deal. He talked to many people about it. He realized that many wise and important men thought it best to say no more about it.

"But sirs," Patrick said to a group of gentlemen one evening in the Raleigh Tavern, a fine old Virginia inn. "If we accept this tax, we are giving up the right of all free-born Englishmen to be taxed only with their own consent. If we do not continue to protest about this Act, Parliament will grind us beneath its heel, and we will wake up suddenly to find ourselves slaves!"

"Hear! Hear!" said several of the gentlemen.

Mann Page, one of the burgesses present, looked angrily at Patrick.

"My young friend," he said with an unpleasant smile that made Patrick's blood boil. "The House has been all over that ground. What we did was approved by the ablest men in the colony. England needs money and must get it where she can. This is the time to bow to the wind and not fight the storm. Not one of us, not even you, Mr. Henry, wants to separate from England. And that, believe me, sir, is the only other thing we can try to do. If we give in, as loyal subjects, the tax will be removed in time. If we resist, England will whip us with all her strength until we obey. And then we will really feel the tyrant's heel. It is my advice, Mr. Henry, that you be guided by men older and wiser than yourself. Other gentlemen with ideas like yours should do the same."

Patrick did not answer. The subject was changed, and in a short while the gentlemen went to their rooms.

When Pat got back to his room, he sat down at his desk. Picking up a quill and a

piece of paper, he started writing down the thoughts about the tax that had been in his mind for weeks.

It was late when Pat finally put down his quill and went to bed. He arose early the next morning and sat down at the desk. He began to put his ideas of the night before into resolutions that could be read in the House of Burgesses. His resolutions told in legal language what he believed about the Stamp Act.

That evening, Patrick discussed his resolutions with two gentlemen whom he felt he could trust, Mr. John Flemming of Cumberland, and Mr. George Johnson of Fairfax.

The gentlemen thought that a few changes in the wording of the resolutions would make them clearer.

"Mr. Flemming," Patrick said, "since you are at the desk, will you be good enough to write down our changes?"

"Certainly, sir, but there seems to be no paper left," he answered as he picked up the quill.

Pat picked up a law book from the desk. It had several blank pages at the back.

"Perhaps this will do, sir."

When they had finished, Patrick said, "I would like to ask you for your support when I present these to the burgesses tomorrow."

"These last few resolutions are rather strongly worded, Mr. Henry, but you may count on my support," said John Flemming.

"You may count on mine, also," said Mr. Johnson.

"Thank you, gentlemen," Pat replied.

At ten the next morning, the Assembly met. Mr. Randolph, the King's Attorney, was in charge of the meeting.

Patrick rose to his feet, and Mr. Randolph called on him to speak.

"I have here, sir, some resolutions which I wish to present. They concern the Stamp Act. It is my belief that we cannot, as free Englishmen, accept such injustice without making ourselves heard. It is our duty to protest by all the means we have. We must protest so loudly and with such force that our

cries will echo in the Halls of Parliament —
yea, even to His Majesty's palace itself."

Some of the members were pleased at the
thought of taking up matters which until now
had been carefully avoided. A few were
shocked and felt that it was treason to speak
about the King and Parliament with so little
respect.

"Do I hear a second to the motion to read
these resolutions?" Chairman Randolph asked.

Mr. Johnson jumped to his feet. "Aye, sir,
I second the motion."

"Very well, Mr. Henry. You may read your
resolutions."

Pat read them, and as he finished, it
sounded as if a storm had broken in the
chamber. The men were on their feet, some
cheering, some shouting angrily.

Mr. Randolph rapped for order. When the
noise finally died down and the burgesses
were seated again, Patrick's resolutions were
discussed. The fifth resolution, which said
that only Virginians had the right to tax
Virginia, caused the greatest objection.

In defending his resolutions, Patrick made one of his most wonderful speeches. He even convinced many of those who had stood against him to support him. He spoke with great strength and feeling, and his words made good sense to most of the members. The chamber was quiet, listening intently to the words of the young burgess. Toward the end of his speech, many of the burgesses felt that Patrick had said too much against the King.

"Treason! Treason!" shouted Mr. Robinson.

Excited shouts of "Treason!" were heard from other gentlemen.

Patrick didn't move. He gazed calmly at the burgesses and waited for the room to be quiet. Then, undisturbed by the outburst, he finished his speech. His eyes swept the room, blazing at each man, as he roared, "If *this* be treason, make the most of it!"

The five resolutions were passed.

CHAPTER 15

Liberty or Death

Sarah," Patrick called as he came home one evening, "I have exciting news! England has decided not to collect the stamp tax any longer. People in all the colonies were so bitter about the Stamp Act that it has been given up."

"Oh, Pat," Sarah said, smiling proudly at her husband. "You helped make it happen with your speeches. I am so proud that I am Mrs. Patrick Henry that I don't know what to say!"

Other people outside of Virginia had heard of Patrick's speeches against the Stamp Act. He became famous all over the colonies as a statesman. His fame brought him money, too, and he was able to buy Scotchtown, a fine mansion in upper Hanover.

But the Stamp Act hadn't been gone for long before England thought up some new taxes for the colonies. These taxes caused more of an uproar than ever. Patrick Henry and the other burgesses made speeches against the new taxes. They questioned the King's right to collect such taxes. The Royal Governor was a bit frightened by the talk of the Americans. He promptly called an end to the meetings of the House of Burgesses. The burgesses left the capitol building, but met, instead, in the Raleigh Tavern.

One of the new taxes was a tax on tea. People disliked this tax so much that many of them decided not to buy or drink any tea until the tax was removed.

In 1773, the Boston Tea Party took place. Young patriots, dressed as Indians, dumped a cargo of tea into Boston Harbor to keep it from being taxed. The angry British closed the port of Boston, which prevented other food from coming into the port. The people of

Boston were left to starve, if need be, until the tea was paid for and the city had quieted down. When the news of these events reached the other colonies, many people sent food and other supplies. The planters of Westmoreland County, Virginia, sent a load of grain for the relief of the Boston people.

In 1774 there was a meeting in Philadelphia to decide what to do about the treatment of the colonies by England. This meeting was called the Continental Congress. Patrick Henry was one of the men sent to it by Virginia.

When Patrick returned from Philadelphia, he found Sarah extremely ill. She never recovered from this illness. Pat spent as much time at home with Sarah as he could. However, as a leader in Virginia, he often had to be away from home.

Soon after Patrick's return, the Second Virginia Convention met in St. John's Church to hear reports from him and the other men who went to Philadelphia. When the reports had been given and the Convention had approved them, Patrick jumped to his feet. He suggested that Virginia should have troops to protect her from the British.

The convention was in an uproar. Some of the members shouted their approval. Others objected. Everyone who was not shouting was discussing with the person next to him what Patrick had said.

Patrick remained standing. He let the gentlemen talk for a few minutes, and then he raised his hands for silence.

"Your attention, please, gentlemen." His voice had a commanding tone, and gradually the men became quiet.

"Mr. President," he said. "We have done everything that we could do to avoid the storm which is now coming on. . . . There is no longer any room for hope. If we wish to be free, . . . we must fight! — I repeat it, sir. We must fight!"

Until now, Patrick had spoken with a calm, steady voice. But as he spoke these words of warning to the gentlemen gathered in the church, his voice rose, and he flung the words

out so that his audience shivered. All eyes
were fixed on the tall, powerful figure of the
speaker. So strong was the spell that his voice
and his words cast upon them, that no one
moved. But all strained forward, waiting for
him to continue.

Patrick again began to speak. He encouraged the men to have faith in what they must do, because right was on their side and God would be with them.

"There is no retreat but submission and slavery! Our chains are waiting. The clanking may be heard on the plains of Boston! The war is inevitable. Let it come! I repeat, sirs. Let it come! It is in vain, sirs, to try to delay it.

"Gentlemen may cry, peace, peace — but, there is no peace. The war is actually begun! The next gale that sweeps from the north will bring to our ears the clash of resounding arms!

"Our brothers are already in the field! Why stand we here idle? What is it the gentlemen wish? What would they have?

"Is life so dear, or peace so sweet, as to be purchased at the price of chains and slavery? Forbid it, Almighty God!

"I know not what course others may take; but as for me, give me liberty, or give me death!"

CHAPTER 16

Dunmore Steals the Gunpowder

Virginia was going to fight. After Patrick Henry's wonderful speech, the Virginia burgesses voted to prepare to defend their colony.

Once, Patrick had been a failure. Now, he had become a great patriot and statesman. His clear thinking, his brave fighting spirit, and his fiery tongue had made him a leader of the people in their fight for freedom.

One man the Virginians had to fight was John Murray, the Earl of Dunmore. From 1773 until Virginia had won her freedom, he was the Colonial Governor. Sometimes he failed to use good judgment.

On the twentieth of April, Lord Dunmore, following orders from England, ordered Captain Collins, of His Majesty's Ship *Fowey,* to remove the twenty kegs of gunpowder from the colony's supply of powder in Williamsburg. Late one night, Captain Collins stole into town with a party of marines and carried away the powder.

The people of Williamsburg soon found out about this. A great crowd turned out and demanded that their gunpowder be returned. The powder was for the protection of the colony. With fear of Indian attacks on the frontier, the colony had to have its powder.

Lord Dunmore sent a message to the crowd. He told them that he had heard of a revolt of slaves nearby and he had thought it was wise to put the powder in a safer place. He said that the powder was taken at night so that no one would be worried. Should any need for the gunpowder arise, it would be produced in thirty minutes. But this message fooled no one.

The crowd did not go home. The people

remained talking. They waved their guns and continued shouting well into the night.

Lord Dunmore was frightened. The next morning he sent word to Mr. Randolph that if there were any insult or injury to himself, his secretary, or Captain Collins, he would free all the slaves and burn the city of Williamsburg to the ground.

While these things were happening, Patrick was at home in Hanover. Sarah had died a short time before, and he was filled with grief. When Pat heard of the trouble in Williamsburg, he was worried. He felt that he ought to go to Williamsburg and find out for himself what had happened. But he could not go, for there was work to do at home.

Several days later, Charles Dabney rode into the village of Hanover. He found Patrick eating his dinner.

"Sit down, Charles, and join me," Pat said to his old friend.

"With a great deal of pleasure, Pat. I have some news that won't keep."

"Can you tell me here?"

"No reason not to. It will be common knowledge in a few days. You've heard that old Dunmore stole the gunpowder?"

"I have heard only a rumor."

"I can assure you it's more than a rumor," said Charles excitedly. "No one knows where he had it taken. Aboard the ship, I suppose. Dunmore says he will get it in thirty minutes if there is an emergency, but no one believes him. The bad part is that no one has done anything about it."

"I know what we can do," Patrick said. "We can call out the Hanover Militia, march to Williamsburg, and take the gunpowder away from Dunmore and his Redcoats."

"Yes. That's the thing to do," agreed Charles.

Patrick thought for a moment. "You get word to the officers and men, Charles. Tell them to meet me in New Castle on the second of May. Tell them to bring their rifles. Then ride west to Louisa and bring any men you can. I'll leave immediately for the eastern counties. The men of New Kent, King and

Queen, and Middlesex will join us, I know. They can meet us in New Kent."

The two men shook hands.

"See you at New Castle on May second," said Pat.

"We'll be there," Charles answered proudly.

CHAPTER 17

Patrick Goes
to Philadelphia

For the next few days, Pat rode hard. He made speeches wherever he found people to listen. He told them what had happened and urged the men to meet him in New Kent.

He arrived at Urbanna, exhausted and hungry. A crowd had gathered on the green to hear him speak. He let the crowd cheer for a few moments as he looked around at the people. There were small farmers, workers, large plantation owners, and wealthy merchants. They had come to hear him speak as an American patriot.

Pat noticed a group of well-dressed gentlemen who stood apart from the others. They were looking at him with disapproval. Pat watched their faces grow angry as he spoke to the crowd. He knew that these men were Tories. They were loyal to the King, and felt that patriots ought to be shot for treason. Most of the people, however, were pleased with what Patrick was saying. Their wild cheering left no doubt of that.

On the second of May, Patrick met the men from Hanover and Louisa. They began the march to Williamsburg. They found several companies waiting for them at New Kent.

Patrick made a speech to his men at New Kent. They answered with thunderous applause. These men were ready to fight, not only for the gunpowder, but also for Virginia's liberty, if necessary.

"I need a volunteer to leave immediately for Williamsburg with a message for Dunmore," Patrick announced. "If the messenger has not come back by the day after tomorrow with proof that the gunpowder has been returned, we will march for Williamsburg. Are you in agreement, gentlemen?"

The shout of "Aye" was deafening. There were many volunteers for the ride to the capitol. Patrick discussed the matter with the older officers, and then made his selection of a young lieutenant. The messenger galloped off amid great excitement.

While the remaining patriots were waiting, several messengers arrived from the people of Williamsburg. They begged Patrick to send his troops home and not enter Williamsburg. They were afraid that Dunmore would order the city to be burned.

These messages saddened Patrick, but he didn't change his mind.

At dusk the next day, the lieutenant returned. He was covered with dust, and looked tired. His great horse was lathered from running hard.

"Sir," he gasped, "I have your answer. The powder is gone. The King's Receiver General is on his way here with three hundred and thirty pounds sterling. That is the value of the stolen powder."

Patrick did not know what to do. He wanted the gunpowder for Virginia, not its value in money. New powder might be hard to buy. But he realized that even though he marched into Williamsburg with his men, he might not be able to recover the powder. Besides, Governor Dunmore had threatened to burn

Williamsburg, and it was entirely possible that he would do it. As Patrick thought about the problem, he realized that the wise thing would be to take the money. New powder could be bought — somewhere.

That night, the money was delivered to Patrick Henry. He signed a receipt and promised to turn the money over to the Assembly for the purchase of more gunpowder.

Two days later, after Patrick and his men had enough time to return to their homes, Governor Dunmore sent this official message to the people of Virginia.

I have been informed . . . that a certain Patrick Henry of the county of Hanover, and a number of deluded followers, have . . . marched out of their county. . . . They have taken from His Majesty's Receiver General the sum of three hundred thirty pounds under the pretense of replacing the powder I thought proper to have removed from the magazine . . .

Therefore, I . . . charge all persons . . . not to aid . . . said Patrick Henry or any other persons engaged in such conduct . . . but to oppose them and their designs by every means.

Given under my hand and the seal of the Colony, at Williamsburg, this sixth day of May, 1775, in the 15th year of His Majesty's Reign.

Dunmore.

God Save the King

If the Governor thought that he could scare Patrick with this message, he was wrong. Seven days later, on May 11, Patrick Henry set out for the Continental Congress in Philadelphia. He had gone only five miles from home when he was joined by two young gentlemen of the county. They were carrying rifles. They told Pat that they would like to ride along with him as a bodyguard, just in case the Governor had any idea about having him arrested. Pat did not feel any need for a bodyguard, and he said so.

"I'm sure you don't need it, sir," John Scott assured him. "But by your leave, we'll ride along with you to give you company."

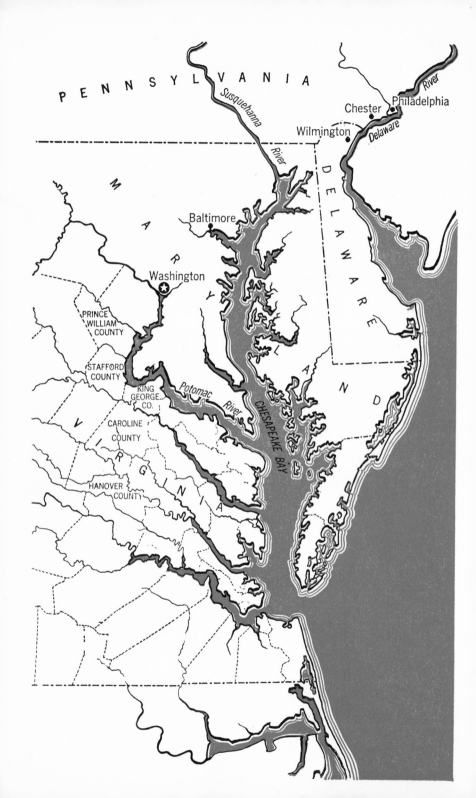

"That I will accept with pleasure, gentlemen, and my thanks to you," Pat replied warmly.

As they rode along the way, they were joined by several other young men of Hanover. As they rode on into Caroline County, a party of five more joined them. The same thing happened in Prince William and other points along the way. It was a large group of men that finally rode up to the Virginia side of the ferry on the Potomac River. As far as anyone could tell, they were simply a group of spirited young gentlemen, enjoying a ride with their famous companion, Patrick Henry. Nevertheless, it was a good thing that none of the King's men tried to arrest Patrick!

CHAPTER 18

Commander-in-Chief

The meeting of the Continental Congress was over. It was June of 1775, and Governor Dunmore was sure that Virginia was in open rebellion. He slipped out of the Governor's Palace with his family one night, and got aboard H.M.S. *Fowey* at Yorktown. In a few days, he sailed to Norfolk. He had one hundred and sixty men ready to fight for England.

The whole colony was arming. Every county had its company of volunteers. Each company elected its own officers, but there was no one in command of all the companies.

Patrick Henry was made a colonel of the First Virginia Regiment, and Commander-in-Chief of all forces to be raised for the defense of the colony.

Patrick went to Williamsburg immediately to take command of his troops. He picked a camp site behind the College of William and Mary and began to train his men.

Lord Dunmore had gathered all the British troops still on Virginia soil at Gosport, near Norfolk.

Colonel Henry felt that his men were ready for action, and he wanted to attack and drive Dunmore out of Virginia. A Committee of Safety had been appointed by the Virginia Convention to take care of the defense of Virginia. This committee finally ordered the attack. Colonel Henry was at his headquarters at Williamsburg when a messenger from the Committee of Safety reached him.

The messenger entered and saluted.

"A message for you, Colonel Henry, from the Committee of Safety."

Patrick took the important-looking letter, broke the wax seals, and started reading hurriedly.

"I don't believe it," he said softly. "They can't mean this." He looked at the messenger. "Do you have any idea what this contains?" he asked him.

"Yes, sir. I was there when it was written."

"Then perhaps you will explain it to me. The Committee directs the attack on Dunmore, an order I asked for weeks ago. But this letter says the attack will be made by Colonel Woodford and the Second Regiment. I expected . . ."

Pat stopped speaking and looked at the letter again.

The young man looked uncomfortable. "Perhaps, sir, they think that Patrick Henry is too valuable as a statesman to be sent into battle. All I know is that they wish you to remain at Williamsburg with the First Regiment."

After the messenger had gone, Colonel Henry sat thinking. He had been so anxious to fight Dunmore. Now he had been ordered to stay behind while others had the honor of fighting Virginia's first battle.

He brushed a hand over his eyes, and then he straightened up. He was a soldier, and a soldier had to obey orders.

Colonel Woodford and his regiment marched to Great Bridge on the road from Virginia to North Carolina. The British had built a fort here. Weeks passed and Colonel Henry received no message from Woodford. At first he was worried, and then he became angry. As Commander-in-Chief of the army in Virginia, he should have received regular messages. Then Patrick realized that the messages were going directly to the Committee of Safety. No one was paying attention to him, since he was not involved in the actual fighting.

One day, Colonel Henry was sitting in the dining room where he and many of his officers had their meals. While he was waiting for his dinner to be served, he could not help hearing the talk of some young officers seated close to

his table. When he realized that they were talking about him, he coughed loudly enough for them to hear. They looked around and quickly stopped talking.

"Captain Gayle," Patrick called to the senior officer of the group.

Captain Gayle's face reddened as he walked up and stood before Colonel Henry's table.

"Sit down, Captain," Patrick said. "I overheard some of your conversation which seemed to concern me. Would you please repeat the story to me?"

Captain Gayle's face grew even redder.

"It's not true, sir. I'm sure of it. Even Congress could not be so stupid as to —"

"Be careful what you say, Captain," Colonel Henry said sharply. "And now, suppose you get on with your story."

Captain Gayle was redder than ever, but there was nothing for him to do but tell the Colonel everything.

"Well, sir, a messenger arrived from Philadelphia about thirty minutes ago. The letters he brought are probably on their way to you now. The man seemed to know what the letters said. He told everyone who would listen. According to his story, Congress is going to raise six battalions in Virginia. The First and Second Regiments are going to be included in the battalions. The messenger said you would have the first battalion, but someone else would be named Commander-in-Chief in Virginia."

Captain Gayle paused for a moment, then he said, "Sir, if all this is true, I think it is a terrible shame! We all do."

Colonel Henry's face was blank. "That will be all, Captain Gayle," he said kindly. "Thank you. But you must clearly understand that we are all soldiers, and we must obey the commands of Congress."

A soldier arrived almost immediately with the letters. Among them was one naming Patrick Henry Colonel of the First Virginia Battalion.

Patrick thought over the situation. It appeared that Congress did not find him useful as a military leader. The six months that he had been in command had all been spent in camp. There had been one fight, and he had not been chosen to command in it. The Committee seemed to be uncertain of his ability as a soldier, for it had taken away his job as Commander-in-Chief. Maybe the gentlemen of the Committee were right. He had proven his worth as a lawyer and a law-maker, but even he did not know if he was good military leader.

The only thing to do was resign and see if he was needed as a statesman in the govern-ment. With great sadness, Patrick Henry left the army in February of 1776.

While Patrick was packing to return to Han-over, a group of officers called on him. One of them read a formal speech telling Pat how sorry his officers were that their colonel was leaving. They did not blame him, but they hated to see him go. The wished him well.

Patrick was deeply touched. He made a simple speech in reply. When he had finished, the officers cheered and asked him to dine with them at the Raleigh Tavern before he left

Williamsburg. Mr. Henry could not refuse.

After dinner, the officers decided to escort Patrick to the edge of town. They had just reached the door of the tavern when they saw a large crowd of soldiers standing quietly in the street.

When the officers appeared in the doorway, a great shout arose.

"What's the meaning of this?" asked one of the captains sharply.

"We want our discharges, sir," shouted the men.

"What do you mean? Have you all lost your senses?" asked the captain.

"Captain, sir," said one man who stepped forward to speak for the group. "We heard that Colonel Henry isn't in command any more. He's our colonel and we don't want to serve under anyone else."

"Now listen," the captain said, not knowing just what to do, "that's no way to talk. We are all soldiers getting ready to fight for the liberty of the colonies. The officers are just as upset over this as any of you, but there is nothing we can do about it."

Most of the men were paying no attention. There was a great deal of noise, and the words, "Discharge us! We want our discharges!" could be clearly heard.

Just then, Patrick Henry appeared in the

164

doorway. Learning from one of the officers about what was happening, he said, "I thought of many things that might happen because of my resignation, but I never expected this. Here, let me speak to them."

With great feeling, Colonel Henry talked to the soldiers. He told them that he could do a better job in Congress than in camp. He begged them to stay and fight for freedom. Then he said good-by.

As Pat left the tavern and walked toward his lodgings, a big sergeant from Albemarle County fell in step beside him.

"Beg your pardon, Colonel, sir, but this group of us was just a small part of the men ready to leave when you do. If you will forgive me for saying so, sir, I think you ought to speak to the rest of the men. If you don't, I'm afraid we won't have much of an army, come morning."

Patrick spent most of that afternoon persuading the men to stay in camp.

Several days after Pat had returned to his home in Hanover, he received a letter signed

by ninety officers of his own regiment, and of
Colonel Woodford's. The letter touched him
deeply. He realized that he had been greatly
loved by his men.

CHAPTER 19

Patrick Outruns
the British

Three months later, in May of 1776, Patrick Henry became the first elected governor of Virginia. He moved into the Governor's Palace in Williamsburg. The Palace had not been lived in since Governor Dunmore had run away to his ship. Just fourteen months earlier, Dunmore had sent out his message against "a certain Patrick Henry of the county of Hanover." Now, Lord Dunmore was gone, and that "certain Patrick Henry" was in the Palace.

Patrick was governor for the next three years. These were difficult times. The new state government had to be organized. Men and supplies had to be sent to the Continental Army.

It was during this time that Patrick Henry married Dorothea Dandridge. She was the grandaughter of Alexander Spotswood, a former colonial governor of Virginia.

In 1781, the year after the capital was moved to Richmond, Thomas Jefferson became governor. Patrick remained in the state legislature as a lawmaker. In May, while the legislature was meeting, the British were very close to Richmond. Governor Jefferson thought that it would be safer for the legislature to meet in Charlottesville.

They met there for about three weeks. Patrick Henry was staying at the Old Swan Tavern, with many of the other gentlemen. Early one morning, there was a great pounding on the door. Patrick went down with some of the others to see what the trouble was.

In the doorway, so tired he could hardly stand, was an American officer. The men recognized him as Captain Jack Jouette, the owner of the Old Swan Tavern. His coat was torn and ragged. He had lost his cap, and his face and hands were covered with scratches.

"What happened, Jack? You look as if you had tangled with a wildcat," Pat said.

"Scratched by bushes," Captain Jouette gasped. "Rode across country. What a ride! Forty miles in less than eight hours, part of it at night, too. My poor horse is done for."

"Why the rush? What chased you?"

"The British. They didn't exactly chase me. They didn't know I was in front of them. Tarleton and two hundred and fifty Redcoats are on their way here now. They hope to capture Governor Jefferson and the legislature. I expect Mr. Henry and some of you other gentlemen would be special prizes. You had better get away as soon as possible."

The captain collapsed into a chair, worn out by his long, hard ride.

"What do you take us for, Captain?" Patrick Henry asked sharply. "I, for one, will not run just because the British are coming."

"Now listen, Mr. Henry. I didn't ride all

the way from Louisa to find out that you are a brave man. Everybody knows that. The point is, if Tarleton captures you gentlemen, we lose our leaders. We can't fight the British without you! With Virginia out of the fight, the British might beat the other colonies."

Mr. Henry and the others realized that what the Captain was saying made sense. They listened as he continued.

"Last night, I was at the Cuckoo Tavern in Louisa, and I heard horses going by. I looked outside and saw some British Redcoats. I got my horse and followed them. One soldier fell behind, and I captured him. He told me that General Cornwallis was sending Colonel Tarleton to capture the Governor and the legislature. I managed to ride around the British and come ahead. I know the country pretty well, so I didn't have to stay on the roads.

"I got to Monticello at sunrise and warned Mr. Jefferson. He got ready to leave with his family. He told me to tell the legislature to try to get to Staunton."

Patrick Henry and the other members of the legislature rode out of Charlottesville just before Tarleton rode in. They went in small groups. Most of them rode toward the Blue Ridge Mountains. They wanted to reach the safety of the Shenandoah Valley.

Patrick rode with Colonel William Christian, Benjamin Harrison, and John Tyler. Tarleton would certainly have been pleased to capture these men.

The four rode hard all day. They had ridden through the foothills and were well into the mountains. They rode up a hollow, hoping it would lead to a pass to the other side of the mountains. None of them had ever ridden through here before. They were tired, dirty and hungry.

As they rounded a bend in the trail, they saw a cabin. Pat wearily dismounted and walked up to the cabin door. He wanted to ask for food and a place to rest. Before he could knock, the door was opened a crack, and the muzzle of a rifle poked through. Pat could see a gaunt woman inside who was scowling at him.

"Who are ye and where do ye come from?"

Patrick, tired as he was, took off his hat and bowed deeply.

"Madam, we are members of the Virginia Legislature. We were forced to leave Charlottesville because the enemy were on their way to capture us. We are tired and hungry. If you could spare some food, we would like . . ."

"Ride on, ye cowards! My man and my boy have just gone to Charlottesville to fight, and here ye are running away. Clear out. Ye shall have nothing here."

Mr. Henry answered her in his most sooth-

ing tones. "We had to run. It would be a bad thing if the British captured our legislature. Here is Mr. Speaker Harrison. He wouldn't run away if it were not necessary!"

"I always thought a great deal of Mr. Harrison until now," she answered, "but he had no business to run away from the enemy." She started to close the door.

"Wait a moment, my good woman," Pat said. "You couldn't possibly believe that Mr. Tyler and Colonel Christian would have left if there had not been a good reason for it."

"No, indeed I wouldn't," the woman replied a little more calmly.

"But they are here with us now."

"Well, I would never have thought it." She stood for a moment thinking. "It doesn't matter. I didn't suppose these gentlemen would run away from the British. But if they have, they'll have nothing to eat in my house. Ye may ride on."

Mr. Henry had used his best arguments. Just then, John Tyler stepped forward.

"What would you say, madam, if I were to tell you that Patrick Henry had run away with the rest of us?"

"Patrick Henry! I would tell ye there wasn't a word of truth in it," she answered angrily. "Patrick Henry would never do such a thing."

"The gentleman you have been talking to is Patrick Henry," Mr. Tyler said with a slight bow toward Patrick.

178

The woman thought for a moment, and then opened the door wide. "Well, then," she said, "if that's Patrick Henry, it must be all right. Come in and ye shall have the best there is in the house."

CHAPTER 20

"His Fame
His Best Epitaph"

Patrick Henry lived a rich, full life. He played a very important part in America's fight for freedom. As a boy, he had been fiercely loyal to his friends. Later, as a patriot, he was firm in his loyalty to the cause of freedom. He was brave in the face of danger, seeing clearly what had to be done, and doing it. From listening to the ideas of other people, he knew what the people around him were thinking. Therefore, as a statesman, he knew what the people wanted, and he represented them well. As a boy, he fought hard for causes he believed right. As a man, he fought hard for American liberty. Most important of all, he had a very great gift: when he spoke, people listened. He was one of the greatest orators of all time.

For five one-year terms, Patrick Henry was governor of Virginia. Three of these terms were during the war years. When he was not governor, Patrick was a member of the legislature, helping to form the new nation.

Late in September, 1787, George Washington sent a copy of the new Constitution to Mr. Henry. The General hoped Patrick would approve of it. Each state had to accept the new Constitution before it would become the law of the land. Since many Virginians would follow wherever the great Patrick Henry led, General Washington wanted to have Mr. Henry on his side.

But Mr. Henry did not like some things about the new Constitution. He had fought long and hard for liberty. He was worried that this document might not protect America's hard-won freedom so that it could never be taken away. He demanded that a Bill of Rights be added to guard the liberties of the people.

The Constitution was finally accepted by all the colonies. The things that Patrick Henry did not like about it were corrected during his lifetime.

In 1794, when he was fifty-eight years old, Patrick Henry retired. The following year, he bought an estate called Red Hill. This was his home for the rest of his life. His health was not good, and he wanted to spend the rest of his days quietly and in peace.

The house at Red Hill was built on high ground overlooking the valley of the Staunton River. Patrick's married children came to see him often. He was happiest when he had his grandchildren with him. He loved to play his fiddle while they danced around him.

His country did not want him to retire, however. He was asked to be Secretary of State, Chief Justice of the Supreme Court, and a United States Senator. Patrick refused because of his poor health.

In 1799, President Washington wrote a letter to Patrick Henry. He told Patrick that he was greatly needed in the government. His ability as a speaker would be of great value to his country. The President wanted him to run for Congress if he felt well enough. If not, he could help by serving as a member of the Virginia Legislature.

Patrick Henry could not refuse this request from his old friend. Although he was not well, he decided to run for the legislature.

A few weeks later, he made a speech at Charlotte Courthouse. He had lost none of

his fire and power as a speaker. He asked the
people to be loyal to the government, and to
guard the liberty that had been won.

Patrick Henry did not live long after this speech at Charlotte Courthouse. He was buried at Red Hill, where his tombstone bears these simple words:

TO THE MEMORY

OF

PATRICK HENRY

BORN

MAY 29, 1736

DIED

JUNE 6, 1799

HIS FAME HIS BEST EPITAPH

Important Dates

In the Life of Patrick Henry

1736 – Date of birth

1754 – Marries Sarah Shelton

1760 – Starts law practice

1763 – Parson's Cause

1765 – Wins seat in Virginia House of Burgesses

1774 – Sent by Virginia as a member of the First Continental Congress

1775 – Attends a convention in Virginia where he gives his famous "Give me liberty . . ." speech

1776 – Aids in drawing up state constitution
Becomes first elected Governor of Virginia

1788 – Opposes the new constitution of the United States. Fights for Bill of Rights.

1799 – Date of death

In the Life of Our Country

1727 – George II becomes King of England

1754 – French-Indian War

1760 – George III becomes King of England

1765 – Passage of Stamp Act

1766 – Stamp Act repealed

1775 – American Revolution begins

1776 – Declaration of Independence issued

1783 – U.S. wins independence from England

1789 – George Washington becomes President

1791 – Bill of Rights added to Constitution

1797 – John Adams becomes President

1798 – Virginia and Kentucky Resolutions adopted

Author's Note

Very little is known about Patrick Henry's childhood. We know where and when he was born. We know a great deal about his parents. We also know that he attended what seems to have been a boarding school until he was ten and that he was tutored by his father and perhaps by his uncle, the Reverend Patrick Henry, until he was apprenticed to a merchant. He was well trained in French, mathematics, history, English, and especially in Latin, which he had learned to speak.

The story told here about Patrick's childhood is fiction, but it is based on known facts. We know enough about the way people lived in Virginia during the colonial days to be able to tell how Patrick Henry probably lived.

Uncle Langloo was real. We know Patrick loved the outdoors and hunting. Although the Indian hunting story in Chapter 5 is fiction, it *might* have happened. And so with the rest of the story of Patrick's boyhood. I made up the tree climbing story in Chapter 3, yet it is a fact that there was a colored boy at Studley *who could climb a tree upside down.* We know Patrick Henry was brave, even as a boy, so this story could have happened.

Historic St. John's Church, where Patrick

Henry made some of his greatest speeches, is still standing in Richmond. It is interesting to note that it was probably known as *The Church* during the revolutionary period. At this time it was the only church in the new town of Richmond. It was not named St. John's until the eighteen hundreds.

There are no exact copies of Patrick Henry's speeches. He does not seem to have written them in advance. Several of his greatest speeches were written down from memory by people who heard them. I have tried to present parts of the speeches in readable form, without losing their flavor or meaning.

I have visited most of the scenes of Patrick Henry's life. Judge Leon Bazille of Hanover County helped me locate many of them. Judge and Mrs. Page Morton took me to Red Hill, where Patrick died and was buried. Mrs. Dorothy D. Herrick and Miss Frances D. Winston, librarians of the Hanover County Library were most gracious and helpful, as were the librarians of the Virginia State Library and the library of the University of Virginia. Mr. William Rachal, Editor of the Virginia Magazine of History and Biography, made many worthwhile suggestions.

WILLIAM PERCIVAL JONES